PRAISE FOR

Grandma Snackie's Stories

"I would absolutely recommend Grandma Snackie's Stories to any parent or educator hoping to teach a wide range of social and emotional skills to their children or students. These short, sweet, and direct stories are highly relatable, with actionable steps kids can actually apply to their real-world problems and situations. The discussion questions at the end of each story really help children understand the deeper meaning and lessons of that story and support them in making connections to their lives. As a teacher, I am excited to use these stories to facilitate class discussion and to supplement a social-emotional learning (SEL) curriculum."

- JAMIE PEKRAS
Instructional Lead Teacher and Coach, Integrity Charter School

"Growing up, my mom (now Grandma Snackie) would tell us stories like the ones in this book every night. These simple lessons began to shape the way I saw the world and interacted with people on a daily basis. I also got to see Jackie act out these lessons in the way she showed empathy and compassion for so many over the years. I can't wait to share these stories with my daughter to help shape her heart in the same way."

- ALEX NOWLIN
Jackie's son

"I remember begging my mom to tell me these bedtime stories when I was growing up. Looking back, I now realize what a big impact they had on me, allowing me to process things I didn't have words for at the time. These stories help teach compassion and grace, and I'm so grateful for a mom who taught me both growing up! I can't wait to hear about the conversations that these stories spark in your own homes."

- EMILY NOWLIN
Jackie's daughter

Grandma Snackie's STORIES

Teaching Children Empathy, Kindness & Resilience

Grandma Snackie's
STORIES

written by
Jackie Nowlin

Illustrated by
Robert Gant

Hardcover: 978-0-578-30050-4
Ebook: 978-0-578-30051-1

Library of Congress Number: 2021921094

First hardcover edition December 2021.

Edited by Jessica Snell
Cover art and illustrations by Robert Gant
Layout and cover design by Natalie Lauren Design

Published by Jackie Nowlin
GrandmaSnackiesStories.com

For my children and grandchildren.
You, more than anyone else, are the reason for these stories.

CONTENTS

Teaching Children Empathy, Kindness & Resilience. *

A Note for Parents & Teachers

Hello there! I am Jackie Nowlin, aka Grandma Snackie. I wrote this book for children, but also for their parents or teachers. It can be hard to know how to talk to our children about life's difficult issues, but I've found that storytelling is a great way to start. In these pages, you will find stories that serve as tools for you to talk to children about the world around them. I found these short stories a great way to explore emotions with children, and to talk about the issues they may be facing. This was a method I used with my kids as they were growing up, and as I entered into a new season as a first-time grandparent, I wanted to record some of my stories to pass along to you and your children.

You will find that these stories represent common challenges kids face in their everyday lives. At the end of each story, there is a simple question or two that will give you an opportunity to talk with your child about the issues in the story. This book is not intended for you to read with your children all in one sitting. Each story holds a different lesson and I find it most helpful to process only one story at a time with kids. Maybe you'll even decide, as I sometimes did, that telling and talking about the same story a few times in a row is what is best. I also recommend trying to find a story that relates to something that is happening in your children's lives or something you would like them to learn.

My hope is that this book provides you an easy way to support children as they learn kindness, empathy, and respect, all while bringing your family or classroom closer together through story and conversation. Keep in mind that not every story will connect with your child at every age and stage of life. The stories toward the end of this book are meant for older children and deal with more difficult topics. Read through each story on your own before reading it to your children and be selective with the stories you choose to process.

I told my children these kinds of stories regularly at bedtime, when they were relaxed and snuggled in bed and already asking, **"Mommy, would you tell me another story?"** I also believe these stories can be told in the classroom when a teacher wants to teach core values that relate to their current classroom emotions and events. Once you have shared these with your children, if you choose to, you can make your own stories with different lessons for you to discuss and process together. Simply start your story with *once upon a time*, use a fun voice and engaging details that they can relate to, and have fun with it! Some stories will be lighter than others, but often it is nice to give your kid a happy ending to help them wind down and give them a sense of resolution. In some stories you can use the standard, *and they all lived happily ever after, the end!*

Good luck as you enter into this fun and powerful practice with your children! I can't wait for you to see all the growth that simple storytelling can hold for your child and you. So without further ado, *let's get started!*

Joey Gets Back Up

For teaching perseverance and the importance of
not giving up when we get hurt or are afraid.

Once upon a time...

Joey's friend Scott called Joey on the phone and asked, "Do you want to come over and play on my swing set with me?"

After asking his mom, Joey responded to Scott with excitement, "Sure! I'll ride my bike and be there soon!" Joey began quickly riding his bike to the end of the street where Scott lived. While on his way, Joey's front wheel slid on some loose pebbles around the large tree at the end of the street. Joey fell from his bike and onto the pebbles with a thud! His knee and right hand were scraped pretty badly. Joey cried loudly, but his parents did not hear him, because they were all the way down the street at his house.

Joey decided to pick himself up, take a deep breath, and walk his bike home. At home, his mom hugged him tightly, carefully cleaned his knee, and gently kissed his hand. Joey's mom said to him, "When I was a little girl, I fell off my bike too. I remember my mom fixing my hand with soap, water, and a bandage. That helped it feel better. Afterwards, I was even able to go out and play again."

After hearing his mom's story, Joey decided he would head back to Scott's house and try to have a nice day, even with his scrapes. When he got there, Scott asked, "Why do you have a Band-Aid on your knee?"

Joey told him what happened. When he was done telling the story, Joey realized his knee and hand did not even hurt anymore!

Scott said, "I am so glad you came over to play, Joey! I really like having you as my friend!" They had fun swinging high on the swing set and going fast down the slide together. Joey was really happy he went to play with Scott, even though he fell off his bike. And they lived happily ever after!

The end.

Discussion Questions

How did you notice Joey being brave in the story? Do you think the story Joey's mom told him helped him to go and have fun at his friend's house, even though he'd gotten hurt? When was a time you got hurt, but got back up to play again?

The New Kid in Class

For teaching empathy, kindness, and inclusion.

Once upon a time...

Josefina was at school when her second-grade teacher, Mrs. Larson, said, "Class, please get into groups of four to work on your math problems today."

But Kinsley, who had just moved to town from Texas, stood all alone. No one had asked her to be a part of their group.

When she saw that Kinsley was alone, Josefina thought about how she felt when she joined her new soccer team last year. Josefina remembered feeling really sad and scared as the "new girl" on the team.

She did not want Kinsley to feel left out, so Josefina went over and said, "Hi Kinsley! Would you like to be part of our group and work together on our math problems?"

Kinsley, who had been feeling left out, said, "Yes! That would be great! Thank you for asking me."

From that day on, Kinsley and Josefina became close friends. Both girls enjoyed being in the same second-grade class together and they even joined the same Brownies troop! And they lived happily ever after!

The end.

Discussion Questions

How does it feel to be new to a class, team, or group of people? When have you felt left out or like the "new kid" to a group? How can we make others feel welcome and include them?

Stay in the Game

For teaching cooperation, teamwork, respect, and making the best of situations that do not go our way.

Once upon a time...

Charlie was the first baseman on his baseball team, the Danville Dodgers. He was very proud and happy to have this position on his team. One day, the coach said, "Team, please welcome our new teammate, Andres, who is trying out for first base." The other boys said hello to Andres, but Charlie felt like he had butterflies flapping around in his tummy. He was nervous because he was the first baseman on the team.

After the tryouts, the coach called Andres and Charlie over and said, "You both did really well! I've decided that you will be taking turns as our first baseman, because you are both good at the position."

Charlie was extremely upset. He threw his mitt on the ground and said, "I am leaving! I am the first baseman! This is not fair." He hurried off the baseball field and sat in a shady spot by the parking lot, disappointed and angry.

When Charlie's dad pulled into the parking lot, Charlie climbed into his big blue truck. His dad asked, "Why were you waiting for me by the parking lot instead of on the field?"

Charlie did not respond to his dad. Instead, he crossed his arms, stuck out his lower lip, and moped.

Later that night, after dinner, Charlie and his dad went for a walk. Charlie told his dad about what happened, saying, "I will have to share my position at first base with Andres and I don't want to."

Charlie's dad told him a story about when he played third base and lost out to another player. His dad said, "It really hurt me and I was disappointed, but after a while I found a place on the team in the outfield. I learned that being part of a team and spending time with my friends was more important than being a third baseman. Once I realized that, I was able to have fun again, even from the outfield."

After hearing his dad's story, Charlie decided to go back and say he was sorry to the coach and his team. He knew he wanted to be part of the Danville Dodgers and be on a team with his friends. Later that year, Andres and Charlie became friends, and even helped one another become better first basemen. Even though Charlie did not always get to play first base, he learned to enjoy playing wherever the coach put him. And they all lived happily ever after!

The end.

Discussion Questions

When was the last time things did not go the way you had hoped? How did you feel? Can you think of ways to make the best out of a situation when things do not go your way?

We are Uniquely Made

For teaching kindness and respect.

Once upon a time...

Melodie was playing at the park with her friend Aiko. They were swinging on the jungle gym and laughing together as they tried different tricks. Then a boy came up to them and made fun of Melodie because of her special shoes.

Melodie had been born with her left leg a little shorter than her right, and she had a lift at the bottom of her left shoe to help her walk better. Even with the special shoes, she had a slight limp, but she got around just fine. This boy at the park was simply being mean. He was also very loud, and he shouted, "What is the matter with you?" and pointed at her while laughing. This made Melodie super sad. Other kids had pointed at her in the past and it always hurt Melodie's feelings.

Aiko noticed the boy picking on her friend and decided to step in. She came up to Melodie, put an arm around her, and said, "Let's ignore him. Want to go over there and play in the grass?" Melodie agreed and the two of them walked away.

Aiko's mom was watching from the park bench and she asked the girls, "Aiko, what happened, and why did you leave the playground?" Aiko told her mom about the boy's mean words. The friends decided to go back to the play area and they started hopping on one foot. They had so much fun laughing and hopping around the park that all the other kids at the park decided to join them. Even the boy who had said mean things was trying to hop and have fun. After that, he left the two friends alone and the rest of their time at the park was a blast!

When they left the park, Melodie said to Aiko, "Thank you for making this day so much fun!" Turning to Aiko's mom, Melodie asked, "Can we come back and play again soon?"

"Yes, of course!" Aiko's mom said. "We can come back next week and have another day at the park!"

The end.

Discussion Questions

Have you ever had a friend who was not as strong as other kids, or a friend who had something that made it harder for them to do things? Have you ever felt like you were the one having a harder time with something? Can you think of ways to make a person feel better when they're having a hard time? It was nice how Aiko and her mom handled this situation. They had joy and fun instead of leaving and not having a good time at the park.

You Got This!

For teaching responsibility and the value of doing your own work.

Once upon a time...

Tamera had to do a science project for her fourth-grade class. The teacher, Mr. Campbell, said, "This project is a big part of your grade!" This made Tamera really nervous because she wanted to do well in her class. She was afraid she would not be able to come up with a good enough idea. For the project, Mr. Campbell asked them to show, in a creative way, what an oxygen atom looked like.

Later that day, Tamera told her parents, "I feel nervous about this project. I want to do a good job, but am having trouble coming up with an idea." Tamera was hoping her parents would come up with an idea for her.

Her dad, Darius, encouraged her. "You are full of great ideas!" he said. "Why don't we draw a picture of the oxygen atom together? Then you can brainstorm different ways to show your class what this type of atom looks like." After looking at the picture they drew, Tamera decided to make a model of the atom. She used cherry tomatoes as the neutrons, marshmallows as protons, and toothpicks with grapes on the ends as the electrons. She built the model herself and learned a lot about atoms in the process. She showed her dad and he was so proud of her!

When it was due, Tamera excitedly took the project to school, but when she saw all the other great projects, she became afraid hers was not good enough. Some of her classmates had a lot of help from their parents and had science projects that were much more advanced than hers. Mr. Campbell, though, knew that Tamera put her model of an oxygen atom together herself and was very impressed! He gave her an A-plus on the project! Mr. Campbell complemented Tamera's work, saying, "I like how you used things that you had around your house to create a really good example of what an oxygen atom looks like. Good work, Tamera!"

When Tamera told her parents what happened, they said, "We are so proud of you! Even though you were nervous, you did your best and came up with a great idea all on your own! Do you see how doing your own work helped you learn more than having someone else do it for you?" Tamera said that she did, and, to celebrate, her parents took her out for ice-cream cake after dinner.

The end.

Discussion Questions

Have you ever been nervous about doing a good job on an assignment? How can doing an assignment yourself—rather than having someone else do it for you—help you learn? Why do you think Tamera's teacher gave her such a good grade, even if her project was simpler than some of the other projects in her class?

New Friendships
Add More Fun

For teaching empathy, kindness,
and the importance of including others.

Once upon a time...

There was a group of first-grade girls who played together at recess. These five girls were best friends and spent most of their time together. They ate lunch together, played at recess together, and walked to the bus after school together. Shannel was part of this group and looked forward to going to school each day to be with her friends!

One day, a girl named Ella, who was not a part of the group, came up to Shannel and asked, "Can I join you and your friends for lunch today?"

"Yes, that would be great!" Shannel replied, and they made plans to walk over to the lunch tables together.

When Shannel and Ella started walking over to the table where the five friends normally ate lunch, some of the girls in the group were not happy. They said, "Ella is not invited to sit with us for lunch. This is our group and no one else can be at our table." Shannel saw how much this hurt Ella's feelings and was upset with her friends for treating her so unkindly. Shannel decided that she would sit somewhere else with Ella, instead of sitting with her closest friends.

The next day, the girls in the lunch group talked among themselves and realized how mean they had been. They decided to apologize and include Shannel and her new friend. Finding Ella and Shannel at lunch, the group apologized. One girl from the group said, "Shannel, you and your friend can sit with us and we are sorry if we were not very nice yesterday."

So Shannel asked Ella, "Would you like to sit with them?"

Ella thought that would be nice, and said, "Yes, it would be great if we all sit together and have lunch!"

Later in the school year, Shannel and Ella spent more time with each other and became really good friends. They would often play at each other's house after school, and Shannel learned it was great to stick up for others even if it is scary or hard to do so. And they all lived happily ever after!

The end.

Discussion Questions

Have you ever been excluded? How did that make you feel? Why do you think it is important to include others? How can we respond with kindness when we see others being excluded? How can we make things right if we have excluded someone?

Pets Get Sick Too

For teaching empathy and how to
work through our pets getting sick.

Once upon a time...

Carlos had a goldfish he got from his aunt Gabriela. She had won it playing basketball while they were at the fair together. Carlos loved his little pet fish and kept him in a jar right by his bed. Carlos would come home from his first-grade class every day excited to check on his goldfish and see how he was doing. He took good care of him and always made sure he was well fed.

One day, he came home and his mom sat him down. She told him, "Carlos, I am sorry, but your goldfish has died. I know this doesn't make everything better, but I want you to know that your goldfish is now in heaven."

Carlos was very sad.

His aunt Gabriela called that night to talk to Carlos and he told her what happened. "My goldfish died, Aunt Gabby. Mom flushed him down the toilet, though. So now he can swim straight up to heaven."

Gabriela liked that and said, "Carlos, you took good care of your goldfish and I am sure he is swimming with his friends in heaven right now." Carlos thought the goldfish probably liked swimming with his friends. Even though he was still sad, Carlos knew that his fish was doing well playing in the waves of heaven. He thanked God that night for taking care of his goldfish.

The end.

Discussion Questions

How do you think Carlos felt when he lost his fish? What can we learn from Carlos about wanting what is best for our pets even though it might make us sad? How can we comfort others who are sad, the way Gabriela comforted Carlos?

We Are Stronger Than We Think

For teaching perseverance and how to have strength in the midst of difficulties.

Once upon a time...

When Lucas was in fourth grade, he stuttered a lot when he talked. He was embarrassed by this and some kids in his neighborhood even made fun of him. The more he tried to stop, the more his tongue got twisted and he ended up stuttering even more. Sometimes he would just read books so that he did not have to go outside and talk to the other kids. Because of this, Lucas grew to love reading and learning.

Eventually Lucas' parents got him special help to work on his speech, and he learned to talk without a stutter, but Lucas still loved to read. He finished a large historical fiction book and told his parents, "I love reading! I especially love to read stories about characters who overcame something difficult in their life and got stronger because of it."

Lucas read so many books and worked so hard in school that he was able to move up a grade. Once in middle school, he felt so confident in his public speaking that he joined the debate team. Lucas became an important part of the team, because he knew many things from all the books he had read. His team even won the city debate championship! He said, "I am so glad to be part of this team. We all worked hard and practiced a lot. We should be proud of what we accomplished together!"

After this, Lucas knew he could overcome most things if he worked hard and stayed positive. His time reading really helped him as he learned about others who had overcome difficulties in their lives. Lucas became a better speaker and reader and he felt stronger!

The end.

Discussion Questions

How do you think Lucas felt about his stutter? Do you think it's difficult to have something that makes you different from other kids? What did you learn from Lucas about overcoming difficult situations? How did Lucas' difficulties make him stronger in the end?

Sticking Up for Others

For teaching compassion, kindness, and that it is not OK to bully others or let someone else be bullied.

Once upon a time...

Carter and his mother worked really hard to find a costume for the school play. He was cast in the role of George Washington and his mom found some used clothes at the Salvation Army that were perfect. Carter was really proud of his costume.

The next day, Carter went to school wearing his George Washington costume, but some of his classmates made fun of him. One said, "Your pants are too short!" while another said, "Look at your coat! It has a tear in it!" Some of the kids even pointed at his costume and laughed. Carter felt like he looked silly.

One girl, Yasmine, saw how mean they were being. She went up to Carter and said, "I like your blue coat, Carter! It looks like something George Washington would have worn." Hearing Yasmine's compliments, the other kids stopped laughing and walked away.

Later that day, on the school bus, Carter asked, "Do you want to practice for the play together at my house today, Yasmine?"

Yasmine asked her parents when she got home and they said yes! She called Carter and said, "Yes, I can come over today to practice with you." Carter was very thankful for Yasmine's help that day. And they all lived happily ever after!

The end.

Discussion Questions

How do you think Carter felt when other kids made fun of him? Have you ever had someone stand up for you the way Yasmine stood up for Carter? How did it make you feel to have someone stand up for you? Why is it important that we stand up for others who are being teased or bullied?

Moving and Saying Goodbye

For teaching resilience, strength, and being able to adapt to change.

Once upon a time...

Alyssa ran home from school, eager to share some good news with her parents. When she opened the front door, her parents were sitting at the kitchen table. She excitedly yelled, "I got a B-plus on my math test!" After sharing in her excitement, Alyssa's parents said they had exciting news of their own.

Her mom told her, "Our family is moving to Seattle in a few months. Your father has a new, important job there. We've talked about it and decided this is best for our family."

Alyssa put her head down on the table and started to cry. This was not exciting news to Alyssa. Not only would she have to finish first grade at a new school, but she would also have to leave all her closest friends. "I don't want to move," she said. "I like it here. I have friends and am on the swim team. I don't want to go to Seattle at all!"

Alyssa's parents knew this would be hard for her and tried to think of ways to make her feel better. They asked, "Alyssa, would you like to write a short note to the teacher at the new school you will be going to?" Her parents suggested Alyssa write about the different things she liked to do and pick out a picture of herself on the swim team with her friends to send as well. That way her future teacher could share it with her future classmates. Alyssa liked the idea. She wrote the letter and they sent it to the first-grade teacher at the new school she would attend in Seattle.

When Alyssa and her parents went to Seattle to see the house and the area they would live in, they stopped by the school to meet Alyssa's future first-grade teacher. The teacher, Mr. Estrada, was really nice and agreed to let her see the classroom and meet some of her future friends.

Alyssa and her parents walked into the classroom and Mr. Estrada said, "Everyone, I have an important announcement. Alyssa is visiting Seattle for the first time and wants to meet you before she moves here!"

● ● ●

Alyssa noticed that her picture and letter were taped to the whiteboard at the front of the class. The other kids in the class were excited to finally meet her and all of them already knew her name. One girl, Kendall, even ran up to Alyssa and hugged her. Kendall said, "My name is Kendall and I am on the swim team here in Seattle! I think we could be good friends!"

Alyssa laughed and was so excited about how nice all the children were. Even though it was hard to move, she felt excited to get to know Kendall and all her new friends. And they all lived happily ever after!

The end.

Discussion Questions

What do you think it was like for Alyssa to have to move cities and schools? Have you gone through a big change like a move or changing schools? How was that difficult for you? How do you think Alyssa felt when Kendall said she wanted to be her friend? Mr. Estrada helped Alyssa's new classmates get to know her by putting her picture up on the whiteboard. How can you help someone going through a big change, like a move, feel welcome?

Teaching Children Empathy, Kindness & Resilience

*

When Grandma Got Sick

For teaching respect, empathy, and how to work through loss and change—especially when a loved one is sick.

Once upon a time...

Emily shared a special bond with her Grandma Donna. They lived ten minutes apart and got to see each other a lot. Often Grandma Donna would pick Emily up and take her to the park. Other times they would play bingo while eating Kentucky Fried Chicken together. Emily loved her grandma very much. She told Grandma Donna, "Grandma, I love spending time with you. I have so much fun when we are together!"

One day, Emily's mom gave her some bad news about her grandma. "Grandma Donna is really sick," Emily's mom said. "She might not be able to come and pick you up as much." Emily's mom admitted that she did not know if Grandma Donna would ever get better.

Emily was really sad, but she asked, "Can I still visit Grandma at her house?"

"Of course!" Emily's mom said. Together they talked about ways Emily could still spend time with Grandma Donna even if she was sick in bed. They talked about how Emily could play cards, draw pictures, and watch TV with Grandma Donna. They could still even play bingo, eat meals together, and talk like they always did. After talking with her mom, Emily felt better about her grandma. As long as she could still see her and spend time with her, she knew she would be alright.

When Emily's mom took her to see Grandma Donna, however, she did not seem the same. She was in bed, and was tired and weak. Even though it was hard to see her grandma not feeling well, Emily wanted her to know how much she loved her. Emily went over to Grandma Donna's bed and gave her a big hug. "Grandma, can we play cards?" Emily asked. "We can play right here on the bed."

"That is a great idea," Grandma Donna said, and she reached out her arms for Emily. Even though they could not go to the park for a while, Emily came over every week to spend time with her grandma. One week, Emily's mom even picked up KFC for them and they played bingo in bed together. They had fun laughing and telling stories just like they used to do!

The end.

Discussion Questions

How do you think Emily felt about Grandma Donna being sick? Have you had someone you love get sick? How can talking to a parent or other trusted adult help when someone you love is sick? When someone is sick, what kinds of things can you do to still enjoy time with them?

Divorce Is Really Hard

For teaching understanding, grace, friendship, and how empathy can really help our friends when they are sad and feel alone.

Once upon a time...

Kai was going through a hard time with his family. His parents were fighting a lot and his mom was always crying in her room. No one at school knew what was going on, but his teacher wondered why he was not doing his homework or playing with the other kids at recess. Eventually, Kai's parents told him they were getting a divorce. His dad said, "Kai, none of this is your fault, but your mom and I just do not get along anymore."

They told Kai that they would be living in two separate houses and that Kai would have to split his time between them. His mom said, "We think this will make things better for us all eventually. We love you and want you to be happy. Even though things are going to be difficult, we promise to always be there for you and do our best to make our homes good and safe places for you."

One day, Kai was late to school and did not have his backpack. He explained to the teacher, "I do not have my homework today. I spent the night at my mom's house, but forgot my homework and backpack at my dad's house." Then Kai started to cry. One of Kai's friends, Samantha, noticed he was crying and overheard what he had said to their teacher. Samantha understood what Kai was going through. Her parents were divorced and she felt sad like Kai did.

That day after school, Samantha told Kai, "My parents got divorced last year. I was very sad for a while, but things feel a little better now. We can talk about it whenever you want to." Kai thanked Samantha for her kindness and they agreed to talk about it whenever either of them was feeling sad. When Kai got home from school, he told his mom about Samantha and how kind she had been. His mom thought it would be nice if Samantha came over some time. Kai liked that idea and invited her to dinner the following week.

Even though Kai still felt sad, he was thankful to have a friend who understood what he was going through. Kai and Samantha continued to talk about their families and became the closest of friends.

The end.

Discussion Questions

Divorce is hard and uncomfortable to talk about. What is a good way someone could ask for help if their family is going through a divorce or some other difficulty? How can you help someone else who is going through something like this at home?

Hurtful Words Because of the Color of Our Skin

For teaching the power of words and the pain that is caused when someone is insulted because of the color of their skin, their religion, or their country of origin.

Once upon a time...

Alonso was walking home from school when an older boy from his school rode past him on a bike. The older boy, who was named William, yelled unkind names at Alonso as he rode by. Alonso had heard these names before and knew that William was picking on him because Alonso had darker skin.

Alonso felt afraid. He ran home and talked to his older sister, Ana. Ana said, "I know how hurtful this is. I am sorry you are afraid. Let's talk to Mom and Dad when they get home."

When their parents got home, Ana helped Alonso talk with their mom and dad about what had happened. Alonso's parents hugged him, and said, "We know this is hard for both of you. We want you to know we love you and are always here for you when you need us." Together, they came up with a plan to help Alonso feel safe while walking home from school. They also decided to ask William's family if they would come over to their house and talk with their boys together. William's family agreed, and, two days later, they came over after school and talked.

While they were sitting around the kitchen table, Alonso shared his feelings about what had happened, and William saw how sad Alonso was. William had heard some other kids at school use the words that he had used towards Alonso. Now he realized that he had never really thought about how hurtful it could be to be made fun of because of the color of your skin. Both William's and Alonso's parents helped William understand how these kinds of words are hurtful. William realized how wrong he was not only for saying what he said, but also for believing that Alonso and others who looked like him deserved this sort of treatment.

"I am so sorry," William said to Alonso, tearing up, "I didn't think through how hurtful my words would be and how much pain they would cause you. I want to do better. Will you forgive me?" Alonso forgave William, and Alonso's dad even offered to meet at another time with William and his dad so that they could talk about what it would look like for William to stand up against this kind of bullying.

● ● ●

Alonso's principal also decided to send out an email to all of the families at his school to explain the importance of kindness and how bullying because of the color of someone's skin, their religion, or their background would not be tolerated. He also set up a special after-school assembly, where both parents and kids could come to learn about this issue and how to stand up against it. This gave Alonso and his family some comfort that the school would not stand by and allow this kind of thing to keep happening.

Alonso and his family also discussed how Alonso could handle these sorts of situations in the future. His parents explained that even though they had every right to be in this country, some people did not want them there because of how they looked and where they were from. They encouraged Alonso and Ana, however, and reminded them that they had done nothing wrong.

Then they made a list of all their family that lived close by and remembered how much they were loved by them. They decided they would have a cookout in their backyard with all the people who loved them, and invited their family and friends. This really helped Alonso and Ana feel loved and valued.

The end.

Discussion Questions

How do you think Alonso felt about getting picked on because of the color of his skin? What did Alonso's parents and the school do to deal with the situation and help him to feel better? What are some ways we can stand up for others who are being picked on for these reasons? Have you been picked on because of the color of your skin or where you are from? If so, it is important to talk to your parents or another safe adult about this.

Teaching Children Empathy, Kindness & Resilience

✳

Parents Have Bad Days Too

For teaching about emotions and how to cope with family members who journey with mental and emotional difficulties.

Once upon a time...

Paige was walking in the door from volleyball practice and heard her mom crying. Her mother said to her father, "You did not get out of bed yesterday. I know you are feeling especially depressed lately and I want to help you. But this is hard for me too." Paige was upset about what she overheard, and went to her room and cried into her pillow. She thought of her dad as strong, but she too had noticed how sad he was acting lately. She did not know what to do.

Later that day, she called her grandmother and explained what she had heard. Paige asked what Grandma Sally thought and why her dad was sad some of the time. Her grandmother calmly told Paige, "Your father loves you and your mom very much, but struggles with something called depression. It makes him sad sometimes, especially when he gets stressed or worried. I wonder if it would be a good idea to sit down with your parents and talk about it. I can be there too. I love you, Paige, and this does not mean your parents don't love you or each other. It is just that sometimes parents have bad days too."

Paige took some time to think about this, and, a few days later, she asked her mom and dad if they could talk. She told them, "I overheard you talking the other day and I want to understand what you are going through, Dad. I talked to Grandma Sally and she said we could all talk together. Can we do that soon?" Her parents said they would ask Grandma Sally to come over to talk that night, as they both thought it was important for Paige to have a better understanding about her father.

That night, Grandma Sally came over and the four of them talked about what Paige's dad was going through. He said that he did have some days when he felt sad and it sometimes prevented him from enjoying life and connecting well with the family. He explained, though, that most days he felt fine. He told Paige, "I recognize that this is hard for you too. I am working on this. I have found someone to talk to that can help me with my sadness and depression. It is going to take some time, though, so I hope you and the rest of this family can be patient with me. I am sorry if this upsets you. I love you all very much!"

● ● ●

Paige thanked her dad with a big hug for explaining what he was going through. She realized that her dad was strong for the way he was working through his depression. They also went to see a therapist together as a family and that helped everyone, especially her father. Some days were better than others, but Paige did know she was loved and it was not her fault.

Paige started writing in a journal to keep track of her emotions, and she learned to better understand her father with time. She knew now that she could talk to her parents and Grandma Sally when she needed to, and that she did not have to keep her feelings and thoughts inside. With time, her father did get better, and Paige was able to enjoy all the good things he did with her.

The end.

Discussion Questions

How do you think Paige felt when she first found out her father was sad? Have you ever felt sadness but were not sure why? What can we do when we are feeling this way? What can we do to help those we love with these sorts of struggles? Remember, it is always good to talk with a safe adult we trust.

Teaching Children Empathy, Kindness & Resilience

*

Acknowledgments

I am so grateful to my children, who listened to all my stories growing up. It is nice to know that these stories helped to create the kind, thoughtful adults you are today! I am also thankful to my husband, Eric, who encouraged me to write this book.

Special thanks to Drew Tilton of Asio Creative, who was my developmental editor and project manager. He kept me on track and had great wisdom in guiding me through every step of this process. A huge thank-you to Robert Gant for his talented illustrating. I appreciate you bringing my stories to life and how easy it was to work with you! Thank you to Jessica Snell, who edited my words. You were quick, so responsive, and just a delight to work with. And, finally, thank you to Natalie Johnson of Natalie Lauren Design, who laid out this book and cover. You are very talented and were so helpful in getting us across the finish line.

Jackie Nowlin is a wife, mother, grandmother, and author who started telling stories like these to her children when they were young. Their enthusiastic response to these stories, and clear growth from the lessons these stories held, encouraged Jackie to continue this practice. Now, with the hope of helping children express emotions during challenging life events, Jackie passes her stories and technique onto you, as you draw upon the power of story to teach the children in your family or classroom empathy, kindness, and resilience.

She lives with her husband, Eric, and two dogs, Cali and Charlie, in Newport Beach, California. Nearby are her two adult children, Emily and Alex, daughter-in-law, Lauren, and granddaughter, Kinsley Rae.

Robert Gant lives in Orange County, California and received his Bachelor of Arts degree in Illustration from Columbus College of Art and Design. He has since continued to build a solid career as a graphic designer for almost two decades. If you are interested in getting in touch with him, please contact the author.